# KENNETH KELSEY
# MORE NUMBER PUZZLES

**Frederick Muller Limited London**

First published in Great Britain 1981 by
Frederick Muller Limited, London, NW2 6LE

British Library Cataloguing in Publication Data

Kelsey, Kenneth
   More number puzzles
   1. Mathematical recreation
   I. Title
   793.7'4      QA95

ISBN 0-584-10763-3

Typeset by Texet, Leighton Buzzard, Bedfordshire and
Printed in Great Britain by
Butler & Tanner, Frome, Somerset

# Contents

# Introduction

Following on from 'Number Puzzles', this collection of puzzles is again based upon magic squares. Magic squares are squares comprised of different numbers, arranged in such a way that all the horizontal, vertical and both diagonal lines add up to the same total, or constant. Some magic squares possess these properties and no more, but for puzzle purposes the squares used must have further characteristics.

It may be useful here to set out all the groupings of 4 power and 5 power squares (that is, 4 × 4 squares and 5 × 5 squares) used in this book which produce the constant:

*Regular 4 power squares*
all horizontal lines
all vertical lines
both diagonals
the four quarters
the centre four squares
the four corners
the corners of the four 3 power squares contained within it
the centre squares, top and bottom
the centre squares, left and right
the two pairs of squares across diagonally opposing corners

A total of 24 groupings of four numbers, given three of which it is possible to derive the fourth.

*Pan-diagonal 4 power squares*
all the above, plus:
any four squares which together form a square
any corner square plus the three squares across the
opposing corner
A total of 32 groupings

*Regular 5 power squares*
all horizontal lines
all vertical lines
both diagonals
any symmetrical grouping of five squares which includes
the centre square
A total of 18 groupings of five numbers, given four of which it is
possible to derive the fifth.

*Pan-diagonal 5 power squares*
all horizontal lines
all vertical lines
both diagonals
any symmetrical grouping of five squares which includes
the centre square
any grouping of five adjacent squares in cross formation
(whether + or ×)
all broken diagonals (e.g. any corner square plus the four
squares lying across the opposing corner)
A total of 76 groupings, after transpositions.

As the reader will discover, some magic squares possess even
more amazing properties, and need not even be square-shaped!

With this further collection of puzzles I have attempted to
explore the versatility of magic squares a little further, and have
devised several new types of puzzle. These are no more difficult
than those in 'Number Puzzles', and like those puzzles can all be
solved by the application of simple addition and subtraction, plus,
of course, a little logic.

Happy puzzling!

# 1

# The Careful Cashier

The hotel cashier was explaining the office routines to his new assistant.

"And here," he said, "we have the safe deposit boxes. Six of them, those that are numbered, are for our own use, and the other unnumbered ten are for the use of guests."

"Why aren't they numbered?" asked the new assistant.

"It's a security measure," replied the cashier. "The keys are numbered, and each one can only be inserted into one particular lock. If it is inserted into any other lock it is captured and a security bell rings in the duty manager's office. So if a guest loses his key, which does happen, it is extremely unlikely that a dishonest finder could use it to open the box, since he would have no means of knowing which box to go to."

"What is the point of numbering the keys if the boxes aren't numbered?" asked the assistant.

"The boxes are numbered," replied the cashier, "but the numbers are not displayed."

"If the numbers are not displayed, how do you know which key fits which box? Is there a chart somewhere?"

"No. That would reduce the security. You will have noticed that the numbers of the six hotel boxes appear to be in random order, but they are not. Their positions tell me exactly where each of the other boxes is. You see, the sixteen boxes are so arranged in four rows of four that the total number of each row, horizontally, vertically or diagonally adds up to 34. So do the totals of the four boxes forming each of the four quarters, and the centre four boxes. There is sufficient information in the position of our six boxes to enable me readily to work out which box carries which number whenever a guest asks to go to his box. Don't look so worried! You'll soon get the knack.''

The position of the numbered boxes is shown below. Would you be able to direct a hotel guest to his particular box?

Puzzle No. 1

| 6 |    |   | 16 |
|---|----|---|----|
|   | 13 | 7 |    |
|   |    |   | 5  |
| 1 |    |   |    |

At irregular intervals the cashier rearranges the position of the hotel boxes as an additional security measure. The diagrams below show the last four such changes. Can you number the guest boxes?

Puzzle No. 2

| 1  |    |   |   |
|----|----|---|---|
| 13 | 16 |   |   |
|    | 5  |   |   |
|    |    | 7 | 6 |

Puzzle No. 3

| 5  |    |   |   |
|----|----|---|---|
| 16 |    | 7 | 1 |
|    | 13 |   | 6 |
|    |    |   |   |

4

Puzzle No. 4

| | | 5 | 16 |
|---|---|---|---|
| 7 | | | |
| | | | 13 |
| 6 | | | 1 |

Puzzle No. 5

| 13 | 1 | | 16 |
|---|---|---|---|
| | | | 5 |
| | 7 | 6 | |
| | | | |

The five puzzles above can all be solved from the clues given, namely that the horizontal, vertical and diagonal lines, the four quarters and the centre four squares, all produce a constant of 34; but if you are stuck, remember also that the four corners, the centre squares, top and bottom, the centre squares, left and right, the four corners of each of the four 3 power squares contained within the square, and the two pairs of squares across diagonally opposing corners, all produce the constant.

All 4 power squares comprising the consecutive numbers 1 to 16 produce a constant of 34.

# 2

# The Controlled Experiment

"Clever chap, that new superintendent at the Horticultural Gardens," said Albert, a gardener there, to his drinking companions. "He came up to me this morning and said, 'Albert, I want you to help me with a controlled experiment. We've successfully propogated this new strain of Allium and now we must find the best conditions for its cultivation. I've put the seedlings into these sixteen pots,' he said, 'each one containing a different number of plants from 1 to 16, because I want to see how they fare in groups of different sizes. I've arranged the pots in a square on this rack in such a way that they all get the same amount of air. If you look you'll see that every row, up and down and across, even diagonally, and every group of four pots which form a square, contains exactly 34 plants. Now, what I want you to do, Albert,' he said, 'is this. Every hour during the morning, take the row which is in the front and move it to the back, and in the afternoon when the sun has come round, take the left hand row and move it over to the right. In this way all the plants will receive the same amount of sunlight and at the end of a week or two we shall see how the plants like being together in groups of different sizes'."

"But surely," said one of his companions, "when you move a row from the front to the back, or from the left to the right, you must break up the groupings of 34?"

"That's just what I thought at first," replied Albert, "so every time I moved a row today I counted all the groups, and dang me if they didn't continue to add up to 34. That's why I say he's a clever chap, that new superintendent.''

"Well, he certainly seems to know his onions," said another, and they all laughed.

The diagram below shows the number of plants in five of the pots. Can you determine the number in the other pots?

Puzzle No. 6

| 6 | | | 9 |
|---|---|---|---|
| | | 14 | |
| 13 | | | |
| | | | 16 |

This puzzle is based upon a pan-diagonal magic square, that is, one which retains its magical properties even when any number of rows are transposed from the top to the bottom, or from the left to the right, or both.

Pan-diagonal 4 power squares continue to possess all the properties of regular squares and have the following additional characteristics: not only do the four quarters and the centre four squares produce the constant, but so also do any four squares which together form a square; further, any corner square plus the three squares across the opposing corner also produce the constant. Puzzles based upon pan-diagonal squares can therefore be solved with fewer clues than those needed to solve those based upon regular squares. Whenever pan-diagonal squares are used in this book, that fact will be stated.

Complete the following pan-diagonal squares to produce constants of 42, 50, 58 and 70 respectively.

**Puzzle No. 7**

| 9 | | | |
|---|---|---|---|
| | | | 15 |
| | 17 | 12 | |
| | | | 18 |

**Puzzle No. 8**

| 5 | | | 16 |
|---|---|---|---|
| 19 | | | |
| | 9 | | |
| | | | 17 |

**Puzzle No. 9**

| | | 13 | |
|---|---|---|---|
| 9 | | | 12 |
| 16 | | | |
| | | | 10 |

**Puzzle No. 10**

| 14 | | 17 | |
|---|---|---|---|
| | | | 12 |
| | 16 | | |
| | 23 | | |

# 3

# The Roman Frescoes

The archeological excavation of a Roman villa in Pompeii had reached an important stage. The last trace of volcanic ash had been removed from one of the chambers and the Professor in charge was studying the wall frescoes which had been revealed.

"Yes," he said to his assistant, "this was probably the sanctum of the local oracle, or soothsayer. You can see the fragments of magic squares still visible on three of the walls. The oracles from the time of Augustus onwards attached great importance to the magical qualities of these squares. It was their practice to choose one square which they considered particularly propitious and then depict its four rotations, one on each of the four walls. From this fragment you can see that this particular magic square was four by four and since the numbers 1 and 16 are both clearly visible we can tell that the magic total was 34. It is a pity that none of the squares is complete, as the Institute has a duty to restore all frescoes to their original design wherever possible."

"If these fragments are all rotations of the same square," said his assistant, "it may be possible to reconstruct them in their original form. I'll give it some thought."

The fragments she had to work upon are reproduced below. Can you reconstruct the original squares as she did?

Puzzle No. 11

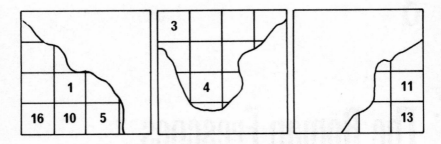

This puzzle requires a little more thought than those in Chapter 1, but it is nonetheless straightforward.

Four similar puzzles follow, all requiring completion to produce a constant of 34.

The solutions at the end of the book show the position of the first fragments unchanged, the second and third fragments being rotations.

Puzzle No. 12

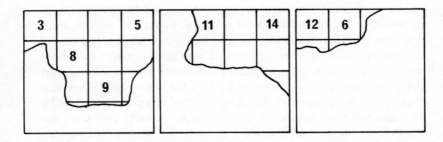

Puzzle No. 13

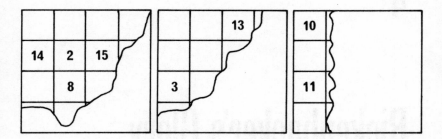

Puzzle No. 14

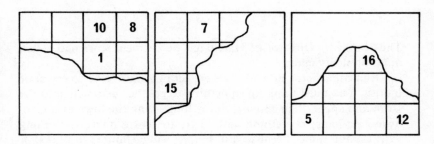

Puzzle No. 15

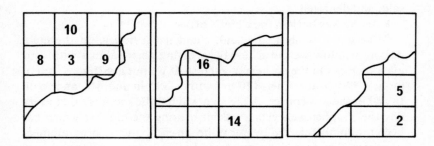

11

# 4

# Rickenbacker's Glory

The Managing Director of Harridge's department store had called in his publicity man.

"Rickenbacker," he said, "we expect February to be a very poor month. You must think up something to get the customers into the store and spend their money. Something along the lines of a give-away, perhaps, something with flair, to create interest. Nothing extravagant, mind, because your budget will be limited to £4,000 or so."

"I'll get onto it right away, Chief, creation-wise," Rickenbacker said, and departed.

Later he was back in the Chief's office.

"I've got it, Chief," he said, "and it's a honey. In the main display window we put a slowly revolving glass cabinet with four glass shelves.On the corners of each shelf we put a different sum of money, £5 in one corner, £10 in another, £15 in another, and so on to £80 in the last corner. A big sign will tell the shoppers that every day the shopper who gets a receipt bearing the number which has been randomly selected by our in-house computer — programmed, of course, Chief, to be nearer the end of each day — will be allowed to go into the display window and select four piles of money, either all the money on any one shelf, or two adjacent piles of money and the two piles immediately above or below them, or any pile from the top shelf and the three piles immediately below it. Imagine the excitement, Chief! There'll be people outside the window shouting advice — choose those four! No! Choose those four! — Boy, will it create interest!''

"Rickenbacker," said the Chief, "have you gone mad? I said your budget was £4,000. Those shoppers aren't fools. They'll choose the four piles containing the greatest amount of money."

"Don't worry, Chief," said Rickenbacker. "I'll arrange the notes so that whichever piles are chosen the winner will always receive £170. Twenty-four shopping days at £170 will cost us £4,080."

"I hope you're right, Rickenbacker," said the Chief. "For your sake, I hope you're right. Otherwise you're fired!"

Rickenbacker works there still.

The diagram below depicts the four shelves of the glass cabinet. How had Rickenbacker arranged the bank-notes on the shelves so that the money at the corners of all 16 planes and the four vertical edges all added up to £170. The position and value of five piles are given.

Puzzle No. 16

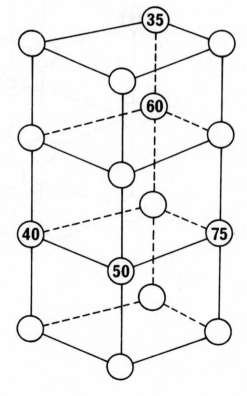

This puzzle utilizes the characteristic of a 4 power pan-diagonal square, namely that any four squares which together form a square, produce the constant.

Four similar puzzles follow, all requiring completion to produce a constant of 34.

Puzzle No. 17

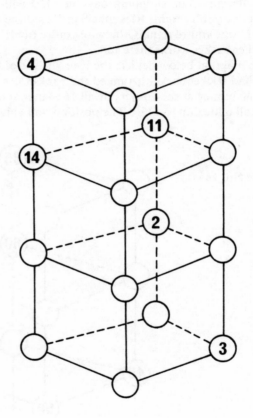

Puzzle No. 18

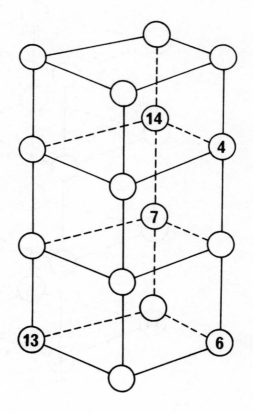

Puzzle No. 19

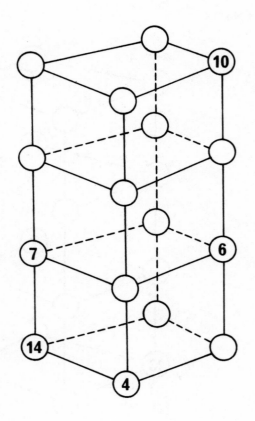

Puzzle No. 20

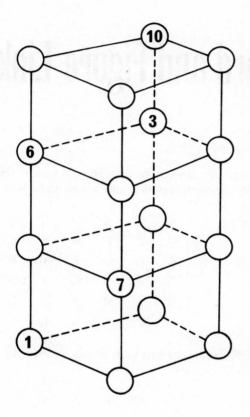

# 5

# Word and Figure Link

Magic squares can also be formed with words, the more usual ones being those which read the same across and down, for example:

| | | | | | |
|---|---|---|---|---|---|
| A | C | R | O | S | S |
| C | L | E | R | I | C |
| R | E | G | I | M | E |
| O | R | I | G | I | N |
| S | I | M | I | L | E |
| S | C | E | N | E | S |

Others can be formed with words which read differently across and down, such as:

| | | | |
|---|---|---|---|
| C | R | A | M |
| L | O | G | O |
| U | S | E | S |
| B | E | S | T |

It is this latter type of word square which is used in the next five puzzles, since it can be converted to a figure square with the aid of an appropriate linking clue. For example, given the word square above and the linking clue:

Native of Bulgaria = 9, 6, 16, 5, 10, 13

one knows that the letters of the word 'BULGAR' (for that is the solution to the clue above) correspond to the above figures. If one then places those figures in a 4 × 4 grid in the squares which correspond to the positions occupied by the letters, the following incomplete figure square is revealed:

|    | 13 | 10 |    |
|----|----|----|----|
| 16 |    | 5  |    |
| 6  |    |    |    |
| 9  |    |    |    |

With the knowledge that the constant is 34, it is relatively easy to complete the figure square:

| 3  | 13 | 10 | 8  |
|----|----|----|----|
| 16 | 2  | 5  | 11 |
| 6  | 12 | 15 | 1  |
| 9  | 7  | 4  | 14 |

Thus the word square leads to a figure square, given a linking clue.

The following five puzzles all require the initial creation of a word square, using normal crossword clues, so as to arrive at a figure square with a constant of 34.

Puzzle No. 21

ACROSS
1 Spiders do.
2 Extreme dislike.
3 Always.
4 A short demonstration.

DOWN
1 Outhouse.
2 Cover with slabs.
3 Detail of news.
4 Roman fiddler.

LINK: Pungent root plant, eaten in a salad = 6, 1, 2, 5, 16, 7.

Puzzle No. 22

ACROSS
1 Large, graceful, long-necked bird.
2 Ring of light.
3 Preposition.
4 Day labourer in Central America.

DOWN
1 Vessel.
2 Diminish.
3 Counter-tenor.
4 Midday.

LINK: At the same time as = 14, 5, 10, 2, 4, 13.

20

## Puzzle No. 23

ACROSS
1 --- scepter'd isle.
2 Competitive trial of speed.
3 The Bard's river.
4 House on a roof.

DOWN
1 Snare.
2 Possess.
3 Religious image.
4 Dispatched.

LINK: Twitters merrily = 10, 9, 16, 8, 11, 7.

## Puzzle No. 24

ACROSS
1 Scottish tribe.
2 It springs eternal.
3 Wild mountain goat.
4 Examine critically.

DOWN
1 Written note.
2 Part of the ear.
3 Copies.
4 Following.

LINK: Religious chessman = 8, 12, 4, 14, 2, 15.

Puzzle No. 25

ACROSS
1 Taps backwardly.
2 Robust.
3 Common metal.
4 Necessary want.

DOWN
1 Climb — up a leg?
2 Peel.
3 Bitter purgative drug.
4 Watch over.

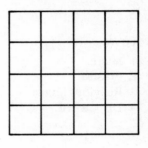

LINK: Impart a shine, not necessarily Slavonic = 6, 8, 14, 2, 15, 12.

# 6

# The Maths Master

The Head was addressing the new maths master.

"I have just heard that the School Inspector is paying us a visit later today and will be testing one boy in five in your class. He is a strange chap whose practice is to select one row of boys, either horizontally, vertically or diagonally across the class-room. Now last year he chose the front row where your predecessor had placed all the duffers and as a result we didn't get a very favourable report. We don't want that to happen again, so do you think that you could move the boys around a bit so that there's a chance that the boys he tests will represent a more or less fair cross-section of the class?"

"I can do better than that," said the maths master. "I have already graded the boys in order of merit, the cleverest being No. 1 and so on down to No. 25. I will position them throughout the room so that whichever row the inspector chooses he will be testing an absolutely average cross-section of the class, neither better nor worse."

How did he do it? The position and grading of 8 of the boys is given.

| 4 | 20 |   |   | 11 |
|---|---|---|---|---|
| 18 |   |   | 1 |   |
|   |   |   |   |   |
| 9 |   |   | 21 |   |
|   |   | 10 |   |   |

This puzzle is based upon a regular 5 power magic square. Such a square comprising the numbers 1 to 25 has a constant of 65. In addition to the normal magical characteristics that the horizontal, vertical and diagonal lines produce the constant, these squares also have the property that any symmetrical grouping of five squares which includes the centre square also produces the constant.

In solving regular 5 power magic square puzzles it is useful to know that the centre square is always occupied by the mean figure, and that each pair of diametrically opposed numbers always total twice the mean.

Four further puzzles follow, requiring completion to produce constants of 70, 80, 90 and 100 respectively.

Puzzle No. 27

|   |   | 26 |   | 15 |
|---|---|---|---|---|
| 5 |   |   |   | 3 |
|   |   |   |   |   |
|   | 7 | 4 |   |   |
|   |   |   |   | 19 |

|   | 11 | 9 |    |    |
|---|----|---|----|----|
| 14 |   |   | 20 | 17 |
|   | 26 |   |    |    |
|   |    |   |    |    |
|   | 7  |   |    |    |

|   |    |    |   |    |
|---|----|----|---|----|
|   | 28 | 11 |   | 22 |
|   | 27 |    |   | 7  |
|   |    |    |   | 30 |
|   | 12 |    |   |    |

| 28 | 26 |    |    | 18 |
|----|----|----|----|----|
| 8  |    |    |    |    |
|    |    |    |    |    |
| 11 |    |    | 24 |    |
|    |    | 25 |    |    |

# 7

# The Coin Collection

"It is my wish," read the Last Will and Testament of the late Solomon King, "that my coin collection remain in the family, being divided equally between my five sons to add to their individual collections. In saying this I am conscious of the promise I made to my eldest son that he would always have first choice from my collection; also to my second son that he would always have second choice; and likewise to my third and fourth sons. I do not wish the division of the collection to become a source of friction and have therefore made the following arrangements. I have assessed the value of each of the twenty-five trays of coins and have numbered them according to their relative values, 25 to the most valuable, 24 to the next, and so on down to 1, the least valuable. I have positioned the trays, which my sons shall be at liberty to inspect, in the coin cabinet in a precise order.

"I now make the following specific bequests.

"To my eldest son I bequeath any five trays of coins of his choice which form a horizontal, vertical or diagonal row in my coin cabinet, or any five adjacent trays which together form a cross.

"To each of my other four sons I bequeath five trays of coins to be selected in the same manner as that adopted by my eldest son, the selections to be made by each son in turn in order of seniority.

"If my eldest son should choose five trays in a diagonal line or in cross-formation, my other sons may reposition the trays by moving any number of rows from the left to the right, or from the top to the bottom, or do both, provided that they can still make their choice by the same configuration. Such repositioning will not affect the evenness of the division as the numbers of all such groupings will continue to total 65.

"By these means I am ensuring that all my sons receive an equal portion of my collection, while at the same time I am honouring the promises I have made to my eldest sons."

When the five sons opened the doors of the cabinet they were dismayed to discover that most of the numbers had become unstuck and only 8 of them still adhered to the trays.

"So much for the Old Boy's weird idea," said one. "Now what do we do?"

"We study the situation calmly," said another, "and see if it is possible to work out where the other numbers go. We all know what Dad had in mind when he wrote about friction, so let's avoid it if we can."

They could and they did.

The diagram below shows the position of the eight numbers which remain adhered to the trays. Can you allocate the other numbers?

Puzzle No. 31

| 3 |    | 22 |    |   |
|---|----|----|----|---|
|   | 10 |    | 1  |   |
|   |    |    |    | 8 |
|   | 23 |    | 17 |   |
|   | 19 |    |    |   |

This puzzle uses the special characteristics of the pan-diagonal 5 power square, namely that any number of rows may be transposed from the left to the right or from the bottom to the top without destroying the square's magical qualities. Since the rows can be so moved, it follows that the mean figure can occupy any square, and not just the centre square. It also follows that diametrically opposed numbers no longer total twice the mean, as they do in regular squares.

Further characteristics of the pan-diagonal 5 power square are, first, that any grouping of five adjacent squares in cross-formation, (whether + or ×) also produces the constant; and secondly that so also do the broken diagonals (e.g. the two squares and three squares lying across opposing corners).

In solving these puzzles it may be necessary mentally to transpose rows in order to recognize groupings containing four of the five numbers.

A further four puzzles follow, requiring completion to produce constants of 65, 75, 85 and 95 respectively.

Puzzle No. 32

| | 25 | | | |
|---|---|---|---|---|
| | 2 | | 10 | |
| 20 | | | | |
| | 14 | | 18 | |
| 3 | | | | 15 |

Puzzle No. 33

| | | | | |
|---|---|---|---|---|
| | 6 | | 24 | |
| | | 8 | | 16 |
| | | | 20 | |
| 21 | | 4 | 13 | |

**Puzzle No. 34**

| | | 14 | | |
|---|---|---|---|---|
| | | | 18 | |
| 15 | | 6 | | |
| | | | 10 | 8 |
| 12 | | | 21 | |

**Puzzle No. 35**

| | 26 | | 15 | |
|---|---|---|---|---|
| 20 | | | | 23 |
| | 28 | | | 14 |
| | 19 | | 8 | |
| | | | | 21 |

# 8

# 5 Power Number Jigs

The following puzzles are equivalent to jigsaw puzzles, the repeated numbers providing the clues as to where the sequences of numbers overlap or interlock.

In the first four puzzles you are required to arrange the sequences of numbers, some horizontally and some vertically in the adjacent grid in such a way that all the horizontal, vertical and diagonal lines add up to 65.

The fifth puzzle is harder in that the sequences could also be inserted in the grid diagonally.

All the squares are pan-diagonal, and some numbers have already been provided as clues.

16, 4, 12, 25.
14, 22, 10, 18.
8, 2, 21.
15, 23, 6.
21, 20, 14.
15, 9, 3.
23, 17, 11.
5, 24, 18.
25, 19, 13.
13, 7, 1.

Puzzle No. 36

| | | | | |
|---|---|---|---|---|
| | 15 | | | |
| | | | 5 | |
| | | | | |
| | 22 | | | |

8, 21, 14, 2.
12, 16, 25, 4.
13, 17, 21.
21, 1, 10.
6, 15, 19.
12, 5, 18.
24, 3, 17.
10, 23, 11.
7, 11, 20.
9, 22, 15.

Puzzle No. 37

| | | | | |
|---|---|---|---|---|
| | | | | |
| | | 13 | | |
| | 22 | | | |
| | | 19 | | |
| | | | | |

2, 6, 18, 25.
7, 13, 19, 1.
15, 17, 3.
14, 16, 5.
2, 23, 9.
20, 24, 12.
5, 22, 8.
9, 11, 20.
21, 10, 12.
15, 4, 7.

Puzzle No. 38

| | | | | |
|---|---|---|---|---|
| | | | 22 | |
| | | | | |
| | | 17 | | |
| | | 21 | | |
| | | | | |

20, 8, 1, 14.
4, 12, 25, 18.
7, 23, 4.
24, 5, 16.
20, 11, 7.
5, 13, 21.
16, 9, 2.
17, 10, 3.
19, 15, 6.
22, 3, 19.

Puzzle No. 39

| | | | | |
|---|---|---|---|---|
| | | | | |
| | 24 | | | |
| | | | | |
| | 21 | | | |
| 22 | | | | |

18, 14, 10, 1.
3, 16, 9, 22.
24, 20, 11, 7.
7, 4, 21.
4, 25, 16.
17, 13, 9.
8, 17, 1.
6, 2, 23.
24, 12, 5.
23, 19, 15.

| 24 | | | | |
|---|---|---|---|---|
| | | | | |
| | 21 | | | |
| | | | | 22 |
| | 2 | | | |

Puzzle No. 40

# 9

# 6 Power Number Jigs

The following five puzzles are similar to those in the previous chapter but are based upon 6 power magic squares, comprising the numbers 1 to 36, and having a constant of 111. As with the 5 power number jigs, the sequences of numbers have to be inserted into the adjacent grids either horizontally or vertically, except that the fifth puzzle is harder, because the sequences of numbers could also be inserted in the grid diagonally.

Each line must total 111, and some numbers have already been provided as clues.

4, 19, 18, 33, 12.
30, 15, 22, 7, 24.
25, 36, 16, 20.
21, 17, 9, 24.
4, 6, 29, 10.
2, 34, 5, 28.
10, 32, 30.
20, 1, 13.
2, 14, 26.
23, 11, 3.
5, 8, 27.
35, 3, 31.

Puzzle No. 41

| 25 | | | | | |
|----|----|----|----|----|----|
| | | | | | |
| | | | 23 | | |
| | | 26 | | | |
| | | | | | |
| | | | | 24 | |

## Puzzle No. 42

16, 9, 19, 22, 28.
21, 29, 23, 14, 8.
18, 15, 35, 20.
5, 25, 24, 32.
20, 10, 26, 11.
8, 30, 36, 4.
31, 1, 33.
11, 27, 17.
34, 12, 13.
32, 6, 28.
2, 31, 34.
35, 7, 3.

| | | 18 | | | |
|---|---|---|---|---|---|
| | | | | | |
| | 34 | | | 3 | |
| | | | | | |
| 8 | | | | | |
| | | | | | |

## Puzzle No. 43

8, 26, 12, 29, 21.
24, 1, 17, 19, 36.
28, 34, 10, 4.
24, 5, 22, 13.
4, 31, 2, 9.
16, 23, 7, 21.
14, 30, 16.
6, 11, 25.
33, 3, 27.
13, 32, 15.
6, 35, 33.
20, 18, 2.

| | | | | | |
|---|---|---|---|---|---|
| | 28 | | | | |
| | | | 25 | | |
| | | 20 | | | |
| | | | | | |
| 15 | | | | | |

## Puzzle No. 44

17, 9, 21, 12, 28.
11, 2, 26, 20, 35.
1, 5, 33, 9.
14, 19, 36, 15.
7, 27, 3, 6.
11, 29, 23, 18.
14, 16, 7.
18, 8, 22.
10, 4, 31.
34, 30, 10.
13, 6, 24.
25, 32, 13.

| | | . | | | |
|---|---|---|---|---|---|
| | 34 | | | | |
| | | 14 | | | |
| 18 | | | | | |
| | | | | | |
| | | | 13 | | |

34

23, 31, 26, 12, 6.
4, 24, 15, 33, 22.
16, 2, 20, 25.
35, 6, 7, 32.
23, 34, 11, 18.
16, 36, 21, 14.
25, 35, 13.
9, 29, 27.
1, 31, 8.
18, 3, 22.
9, 30, 5.
17, 19, 28.
8, 10, 28.

| | | | 25 | | |
|---|---|---|---|---|---|
| | 9 | | | | |
| | | | | | |
| | | | | 32 | |
| 1 | | | | | |
| | | | 18 | | |

# 10

# The Measuring Device

"I say, Jack," said Sam to his friend and colleague at the Aerospace Laboratories. "Do you remember that measuring device I dreamed up some little while back?"

"Not really," said Jack. "Remind me."

"Well, it was for measuring the changes in temperature, potential and so on, in components under stress. Basically it was a series of micro-sensors set out as in these layout drawings. The sensors were linked in four different series; first, all sensors along the same circumference; secondly, all sensors along the same radius; thirdly, all sensors forming part of the same clockwise spiral; and lastly, those forming part of the same anti-clockwise spiral. All the sensors were linked to the computer which recorded and assessed any variations between the readings of the various sensor linkings during testing, and so it was easy to calculate the origin, extent and location of any hot-spots or weaknesses."

"Yes, I remember it now," said Jack. "So what's the problem?"

"Well, the number and position of the sensors has to be varied, depending upon the size of the component being tested. Sometimes it's 16, sometimes 25, or 36, 49, 64, or even 81 for the really big ones. What's happening is that when the sensors are changed, errors are being made in linking up the new sets of sensors, and so we're getting false readings. The Old Man's just told me I've got to make it idiot-proof, or else! You're the brains around here. Any ideas?"

Jack studied the layouts for a while, then said, "It's easy. Number all the sensors consecutively and feed that information into the computer. Then before each test, get a check-reading from the computer of the numerical link-up. If you don't get 16 readings of 34 when using 16 sensors, and 20 readings of 65 when using 25 sensors, and so on, then you know the linking is incorrect. Mind you, you'll need to work out all the various positions in advance. I'd work them out for you, but I haven't really got time. I'll start each one off for you, though, and leave you to finish them. O.K.?"

Each of Jack's seven incomplete layouts is shown below. As you go through them one by one, you will see the problem facing Sam and be able to pit your wits against his in arriving at a satisfactory completion of each one.

Puzzle No. 46

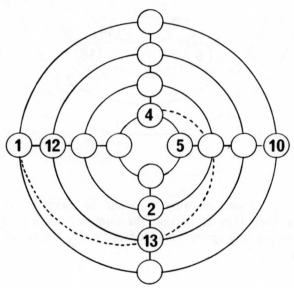

For the first layout drawing above Sam was required to position the missing numbers from 1 to 16 in such a way that the numbers along each radius, circumference and spiral, one of which is shown dotted, all added up to 34, giving 16 such groupings, or linkings.

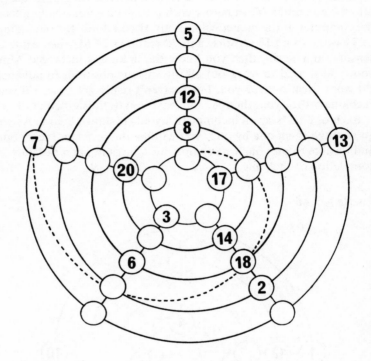

From the second drawing Sam had to position the missing numbers from 1 to 25 so that the numbers along each radius, circumference and spiral all added up to 65, a total of 20 such groupings.

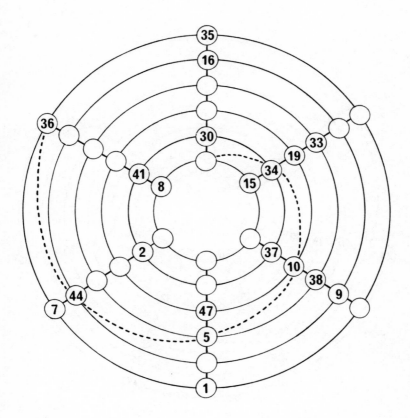

Sam found this layout a little harder to complete. He had to supply the missing numbers so that the numbers along each radius, circumference and spiral added up to 150, a total of 24 such groupings, but the numbers were not in a continuous series, being 36 of the numbers from 1 to 49.

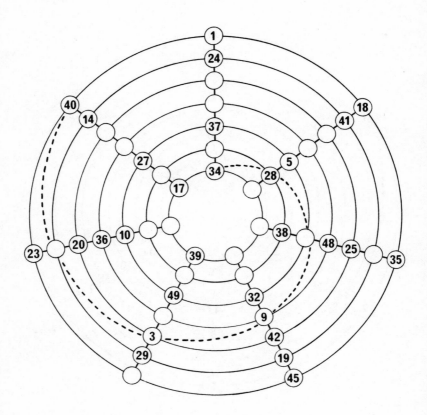

By the time Sam had reached this stage he was beginning to get the hang of it. He knew that he had to position the missing numbers between 1 and 49 in such a way that all the radii, circumferences and spirals added up to 175, a total of 28 such groupings, or linkings.

Puzzle No. 50

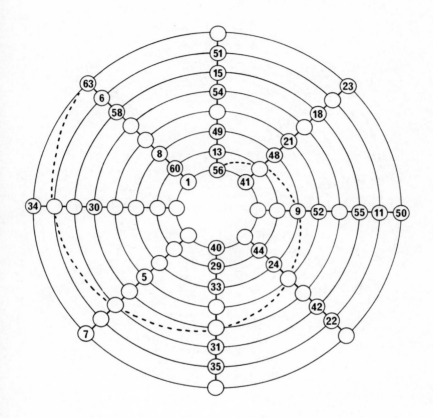

Sam found this layout drawing relatively easy to complete, because although he had to position the missing numbers between 1 and 64 in such a way that the totals of the numbers along each radius, spiral and circumference added up to 260, a total of 32 such groupings, Jack had told him that the totals half way along each radius was 130.

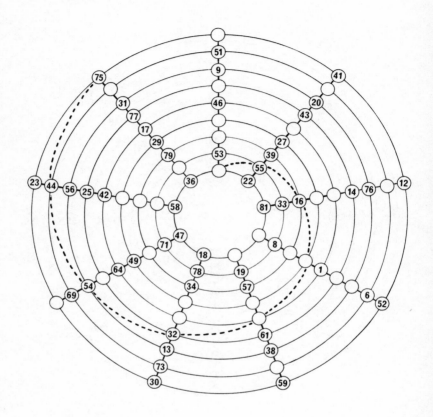

Sam completed his task by positioning the missing numbers from 1 to 81 so that the numbers along each radius, circumference and spiral, a total of 36 such groupings, added up to 369.

The measuring device had been made idiot-proof!

'Planetarium' puzzles such as these can be formed only from pan-diagonal squares. The radii correspond to the horizontal lines of the square, the circumferences or orbits correspond to the vertical lines and the spirals correspond to the diagonals and broken diagonals. So, in theory at least, they should be as easy to solve as standard magic square puzzles, but they appear not to be so. If you are really at a loss to find the solution to any one of these puzzles, convert the planetarium to a standard square and the missing numbers will become more apparent. Look for the broken diagonals.

It is not possible to form a pan-diagonal 6 power square from the numbers 1 to 36, which is why the series in Puzzle No. 48 is a broken series.

# 11

# Magic Crystals

Using all the numbers from 1 to 16, supply the missing numbers in the following diagrams so that the corners of all seven rectangles contained within each magic crystal add up to 34.

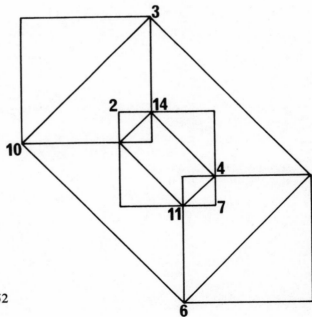

Puzzle No. 52

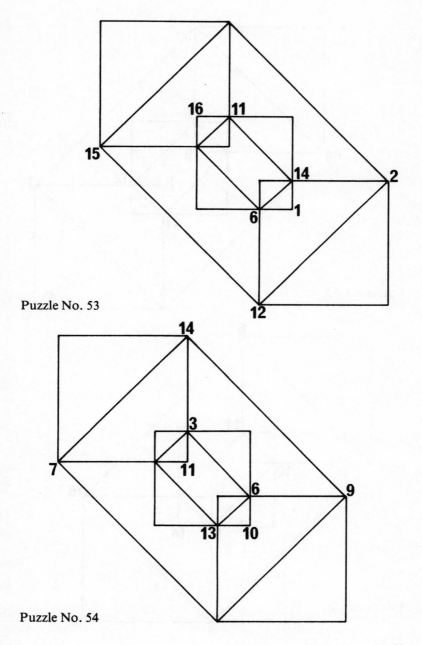

Puzzle No. 53

Puzzle No. 54

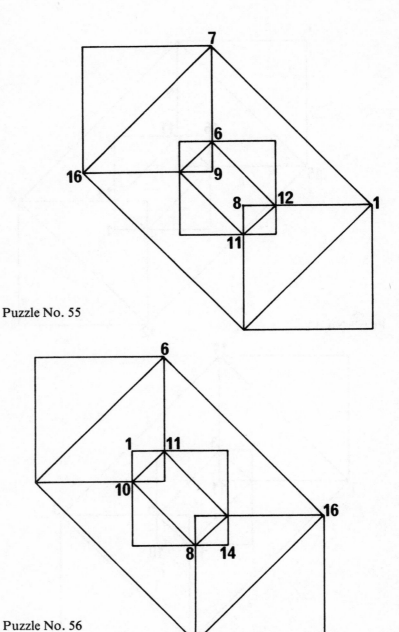

Puzzle No. 55

Puzzle No. 56

# 12

# T'ang Li's New Star

Ancient manuscripts* tell of how the citizens of Liang Chang were once subject to an annual tribute of one pure sapphire to T'ang Li, the War Lord. The first sapphire was to be of 1 carat, the second of 2 carats, the third of 3 carats, and so on for as long as T'ang Li should live. After 25 years the citizens could no longer afford to make their tribute and, by a stratagem, had obtained their release by setting all the sapphires in a star for T'ang Li's turban, with the great sapphire of 25 carats in the centre and the others so arranged about it that in every direction, along every line, the weight of the sapphires was exactly 65 carats. Thus:

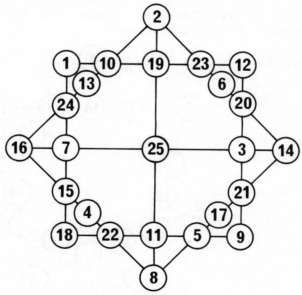

---

*see 'Number Puzzles', Chapter 7.

"I feel the bitter wind of penury throughout my palace," said T'ang Li to his chamberlain. "It is a matter of great regret that I absolved the citizens of Liang Chang from making their annual tribute these two years past. Had I not done so I would now possess two further sapphires, one of 26 carats and one of 27. With 53 carats weight of such gems I would have the means to gather and provision an army for another expedition, and thus replenish my coffers from the spoils of war. I have oft-times pondered upon the merits of prising some of the stones from the Star for that very purpose, but then my impoverishment would be visible to my enemies, and even worse, to my friends. Moreover, I dare not risk offending the Gods by destroying the mystical balance of the Star."

"Master," said the High Chamberlain, "disquiet yourself no further for I can perceive a way of removing the great sapphire and three others, weighing together 53 carats, and rearranging the gems in the form of another star, so that still in every direction, along every line, the weight of the sapphires is exactly 65 carats. Thus the Gods will continue in their approbation, and upon your victorious return neither friends nor enemies will have cause to question your great wealth."

How did the High Chamberlain rearrange the stones? The position and weight of 12 of them is given.

Puzzle No. 57

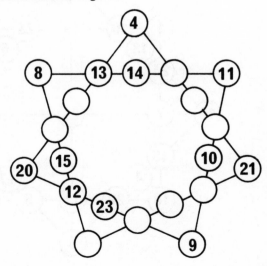

Four similar puzzles follow requiring completion to produce constants of 70, 80, 90 and 100 respectively.

Puzzle No. 58

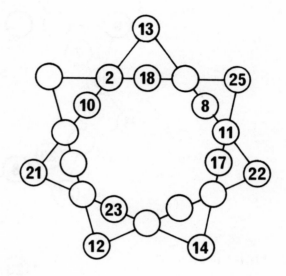

Puzzle No. 59

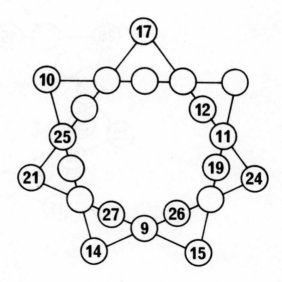

Puzzle No. 60

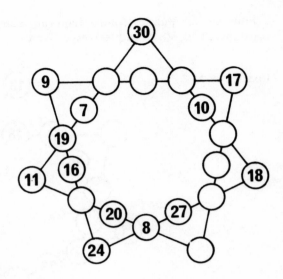

Puzzle No. 61

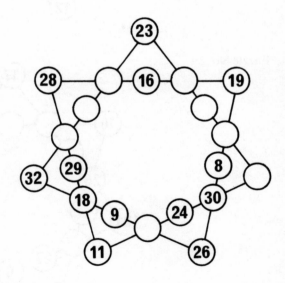

The original Star of T'ang Li was produced by a simple and fairly obvious variation of a pan-diagonal 5 power square. This new star is a further variation, but one not so obvious.

Had T'ang Li needed to take out 7 stones the High Chamberlain would no doubt have rearranged the Star as follows, still retaining the mystical total of 65.

Puzzle No. 62

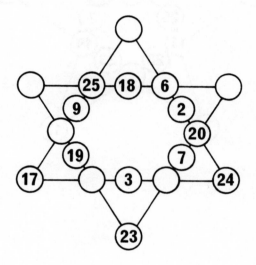

and had 10 stones been needed, the High Chamberlain could always have suggested the following, still retaining the mystical total of 65, which goes to show how versatile magic squares can be.

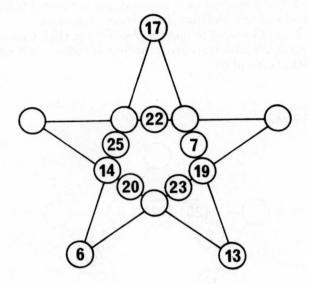

# 13

# The Mindong Evacuation

A company of 450 Marine Commandos was beleaguered on the island of Mindong, and a worried C.O. was briefing his officers.

"At 05.30 hours," he said, "I received a long signal from Corps H.Q. informing me that an attempt will be made to airlift us off the island by helicopter troopships during the next five nights. It cannot be done quicker than that as 90 men each night is the maximum that the carrier can accept from us, bearing in mind that they are involved with other evacuations in the area, besides our own. Five helicopters have been specifically allocated to the task. Although each one can carry 90 men, H.Q. does not want to send in one helicopter each night to airlift the men in groups of 90, as this would mean exposing the helicopters in a vulnerable position on the ground for far too long, and also, to minimise losses in the event of enemy air-attack, they want us to remain dispersed over the island.

"So these are our instructions:

"On the first night we are to section off the island in a five by five grid pattern and position ourselves at pick-up points at the centre of each of the twenty-five sections. The five helicopters will approach under cover of darkness in line astern. They do not know the direction of their approach as this will largely be determined by enemy patrols and other activity in the area. As the pick-up points hear the helicopters approach, each will signal its position by flashlight. As they see these, the helicopters will land at the nearest line of five pick-up points — that could be horizontally, vertically or diagonally as one would look at it on the map — and airlift exactly 90 men back to the carrier. After clearance the men will transfer to one helicopter which will fly them back to the mainland and remain there.

"On the second night we are to section off the island in a four by four grid pattern and position ourselves at pick-up points at the centre of each of the sixteen sections. Four helicopters will approach under cover of darkness in line astern from an indeterminable direction. We will again signal our positions by means of flashlights and the helicopters will land at the nearest line of four pick-up points and airlift exactly 90 men back to the carrier. After clearance the men will transfer to one helicopter which will fly them back to the mainland and remain there.

"The process will be repeated on each of the following nights. On the third night we are to position ourselves at nine pick-up points in a three by three grid. Three helicopters will land at the nearest line of three, and airlift exactly 90 men to the carrier for transfer to the mainland. On the fourth night we are to position ourselves at four pick-up points in a two by two grid. Two helicopters will land at the nearest pair and airlift exactly 90 men to the carrier for transfer to the mainland. On the fifth night the remaining 90 men will collect at one pick-up point and be airlifted by the last remaining helicopter directly to the mainland."

As the C.O. paused, his second-in-command said, "If the helicopters are to pick up exactly 90 men each trip it would seem to indicate that we must position ourselves uniformly at each pick-up point, yet we know that there are parts of the island where the terrain will not permit more than 6 to 8 men to be positioned and still allow a helicopter to land. In any case, if 90 men are airlifted the first night, there is no way we can uniformly distribute 360 men over 16 pick-up points on the second night. So it is clear that we must distribute ourselves in a random pattern, but this carries the risk that the helicopters could land at groupings containing less than 90 men, and if this happens it would mean some men would be forced to stay on the island and take their chances, for there is no way of making up any shortfalls."

The C.O. said, "The final part of the signal set out the exact positions we were to take up, but our batteries were just about run down by this time and we were only able to receive snatches of the last part of the transmission. I've given what we did receive to Intelligence to try to fill in the gaps. I only hope they come up with the answer in time for us to position the men tonight."

He need not have worried. When the enemy invaded the island six days later, it was completely deserted.

The following diagrams were built up from the parts of the signal which were received and given to Intelligence to work upon. What solution did they arrive at?

Puzzle No. 64

| | | 26 | | 12 |
|---|---|---|---|---|
| | 25 | | | 29 |
| 30 | | | 28 | |
| | | | | |
| | 19 | | | 16 |

| | 28 | | 21 |
|---|---|---|---|
| | | | |
| 22 | | | 16 |
| 24 | | 17 | |

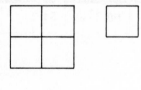

| | | |
|---|---|---|
| 28 | 30 | |
| | | 27 |

Magic squares of different powers can be related in a variety of ways, and this puzzle demonstrates one of them, namely that squares of different powers can produce the same constant from consecutive numbers taken from the same series. The constant in this puzzle can be termed the Lowest Common Constant for squares of the 3rd, 4th and 5th powers.

Four other puzzles which demonstrate the relationship between squares of different powers, follow.

The first comprises an 8 power square, which encloses a 6 power square, which encloses a 4 power square, with constants of 260, 195 and 130 respectively. The 4 power square conforms to the normal rules and is the first one which should be solved. The numbers utilised are 1 to 64.

Puzzle No. 65

| | | | | | | | |
|---|---|---|---|---|---|---|---|
| | 52 | | 56 | | 12 | | 58 |
| 63 | | 18 | | 42 | | 49 | |
| | | 25 | | | 32 | 20 | 64 |
| 59 | 41 | | | 27 | | | |
| | | | | 40 | | 44 | 8 |
| 14 | 22 | | 28 | | 35 | | |
| 55 | | | 48 | | 46 | | |
| | | 60 | | 54 | | 3 | |

The second comprises a 3 power square within a 5 power square within a 7 power square within a 9 power square, with constants of 123, 205, 287 and 369 respectively. The numbers utilised are 1 to 81.

Puzzle No. 66

| 5 |    | 11 |    | 10 |    | 12 |    |    |
|----|----|----|----|----|----|----|----|----|
| 67 |    |    | 28 |    | 23 |    |    |    |
|    | 64 | 47 |    | 48 |    |    |    | 75 |
| 73 |    |    | 40 |    |    | 36 | 58 |    |
|    | 63 | 32 |    | 41 | 37 |    |    | 16 |
| 6 |    |    |    |    |    | 33 | 57 |    |
|    | 65 |    | 52 |    | 53 |    |    | 14 |
| 8 |    | 21 |    | 22 |    | 55 | 56 |    |
|    | 1 |    | 4 |    | 2 |    | 3 |    |

The third puzzle involves distributing the numbers 1 to 50 between squares of the 3rd, 4th and 5th orders, as in the grids below, and producing from them magic squares with constants of 42, 91 and 157 respectively.

| 1 | 2 | 3 |
|---|---|---|
| 13 | 14 | 15 |
| 25 | 26 | 27 |

| 4 | 5 | 6 | 7 |
|---|---|---|---|
| 16 | 17 | 18 | 19 |
| 28 | 29 | 30 | 31 |
| 37 | 38 | 39 | 40 |

| 8 | 9 | 10 | 11 | 12 |
|---|---|---|---|---|
| 20 | 21 | 22 | 23 | 24 |
| 32 | 33 | 34 | 35 | 36 |
| 41 | 42 | 43 | 44 | 45 |
| 46 | 47 | 48 | 49 | 50 |

| 2 |   |   |
|---|---|---|
|   | 14 | 1 |
|   |   |   |

| 4 |   |   | 19 |
|---|---|---|---|
|   |   |   | 6 |
|   |   | 40 |   |
|   | 7 |   | 30 |

| 49 | 45 |   | 21 |   |
|---|---|---|---|---|
| 33 | 22 |   |   | 41 |
|   |   | 42 |   |   |
| 43 |   | 24 |   | 47 |
| 20 | 9 |   | 44 | 36 |

Puzzle No. 67

The last puzzle in this chapter demonstrates that it is possible to distribute a series of consecutive numbers between a square of one power and a square of one higher power, both producing the same constant.

In this puzzle the series 70 to 110 is used, and the constant of both the 4 power square and the 5 power square is 410. Both are pan-diagonal.

58

Puzzle No. 68

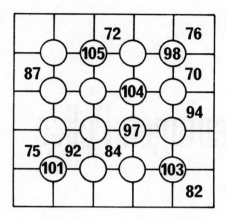

# 14

# The Pentagon Police

It is common knowledge that the Pentagon in Washington is so named because of the shape of the building complex. What is not widely known is that the corridors within the complex are so arranged that they divide the building into eight separate pentagons, with a security control post located at each point and intersection, 15 in all, as set out in the diagram below. By a long-standing Army Ordinance the security police force of 300 men has to be deployed so that at all times a force of 100 men are positioned at the corners of each of the eight pentagons, so as to meet any emergency within that section. Until recently this Ordinance was satisfied by the simple and logical expedient of positioning 20 men in each of the control posts.

However, at the routine military briefing in the Oval Office last July, the President said to the Army Chief of Staff, "About the security police in the Pentagon, General. I'm not so sure that it is wise to position them so uniformly throughout the complex. Any enemy infiltrating the building knows exactly where they are and in what strength. I think you should redeploy them so that no two control posts contain the same number of men."

'Mr. President," said the General, "if it is possible to do that without breaching the Ordinance I will of course carry out your wishes. If not, I'll have to report back to you."

He did not have to.

The number of men in 8 of the control posts is shown, and although for reasons of military security no additional information can be given, any enemy infiltrator worth his salt should be able to work out the rest.

Puzzle No. 69

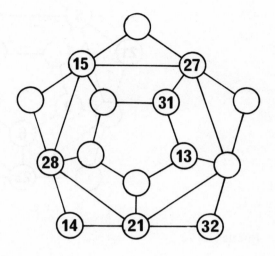

Four similar magic pentagon puzzles follow, requiring completion to produce constants of 70, 80, 90 and 100 respectively.

Puzzle No. 70

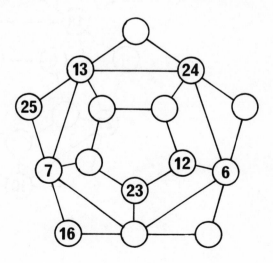

Puzzle No. 71

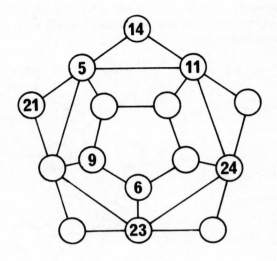

Puzzle No. 72

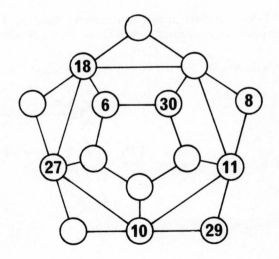

Puzzle No. 73

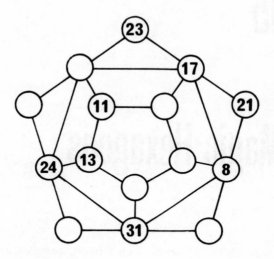

# 15

# Magic Hexagons

Using all the numbers from 1 to 30, complete the magic hexagons below so that the points of all 9 hexagons contained within each one add up to 93.

Puzzle No. 74

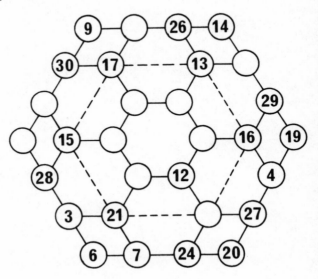

Puzzle No. 75

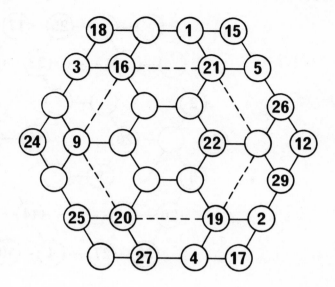

Puzzle No. 76

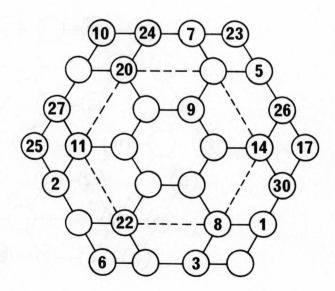

Puzzle No. 77

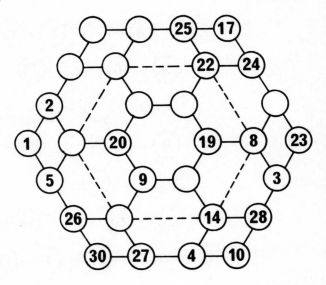

Puzzle No. 78

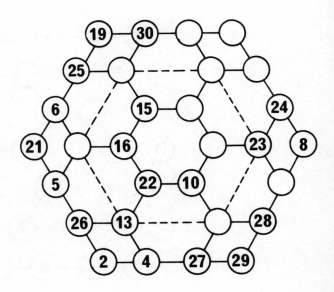

As we have seen, in a 6 power magic square comprising the numbers 1 to 36, the constant is 111.

Question: Why is it, when the numbers 31 to 36 are removed, as in the last five puzzles, the constant is reduced by only 18 and not by the average of 31 to 36?

# 16

# The Incredible Adding Bee

When the ladies of the Oxbridge Entomological Society returned recently from their expedition to Central America they brought back five specimens of the hives of the Incredible Adding Bee (gen. apis arithmeticus) so named because of the precise numerical accuracy with which the Queen Bee deposits her eggs. She selects one empty hexagonal cell and in each of the six cells which surround it she deposits a different number of eggs. She continues in this fashion until she has filled 36 cells all containing a different number of eggs, and then starts the process over again. The incredible aspect of this ritual, the purpose of which is not yet understood, is that the eggs in the cells surrounding each empty cell always total exactly 111, despite the fact that each occupied cell can form part of three such groupings.

When the five specimens were unpacked it was discovered that the contents of several cells had perished in transit, but fortunately a sufficient number of cells survived intact to enable the ladies to ascertain the total number of eggs which were originally deposited in each cell.

From the following diagrams of the specimens as they were unpacked, can you supply the missing data?

Puzzle No. 79

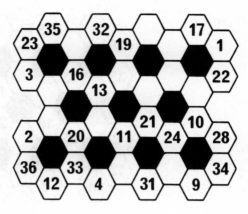

Puzzle No. 80

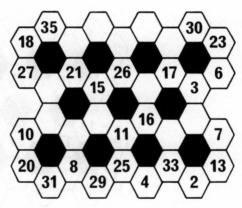

Puzzle No. 81

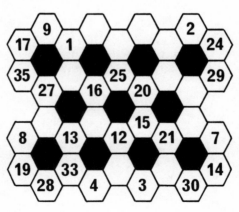

Puzzle No. 82

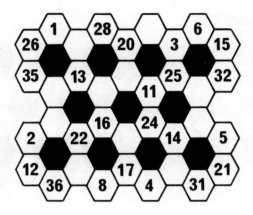

Puzzle No. 83

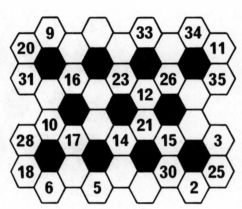

# 17

# Magic Stars

It is possible to form magic stars of almost any size or complexity. The following puzzles set out a few in a progressive order, requiring completion to produce the constant shown in the centre of each respective star.

Puzzle No. 84

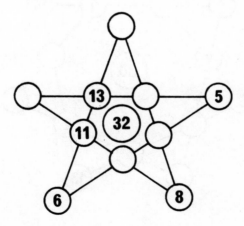

Puzzle No. 85

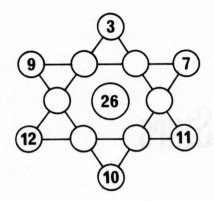

Puzzle No. 86

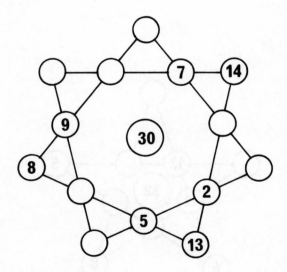

Puzzle No. 87

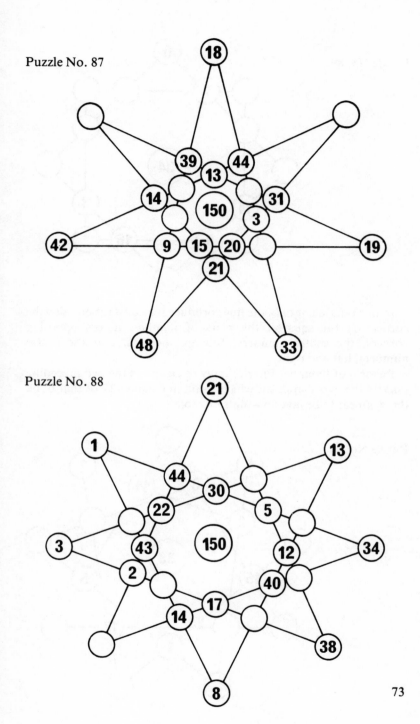

Puzzle No. 88

Puzzle No. 89

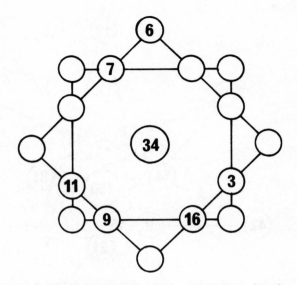

In this puzzle not only the lines produce the constant but also the corners of the squares, the pairs of numbers across opposing corners, the centre numbers, top and bottom, and the centre numbers, left and right.

Readers of 'Number Puzzles' may recognise in the two preceding puzzles the two shapes for which I said in Chapter 17 of that book there appear to be no cross-sums possible!

Puzzle No. 90

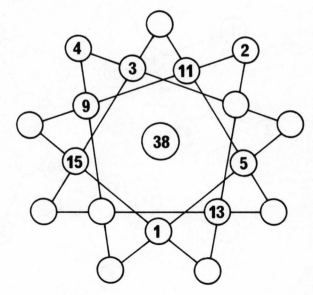

Puzzle No. 91

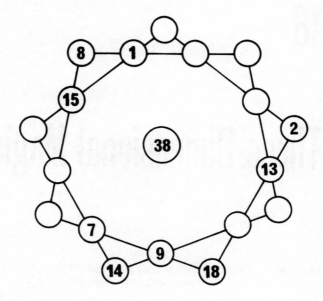

With the exception of Puzzles 84, 87 and 88, the puzzles in this Chapter all comprise the natural series 1 to n.

# 18

# Three-Dimensional Magic

The puzzles in this Chapter demonstrate a few of the many three-dimensional arrangements possible with magic squares. The first three are three-dimensional in that they utilise solid forms, the arrangement of numbers being confined to the surface of those solids. The remaining puzzles are three-dimensional in the truest sense, the constants being produced from combinations which pass through the solids.

The first puzzle depicts a cube in two-dimensional form. Each of the six faces of the cube displays a different magic square, and all bordering squares have the same value as the squares they touch. Given one completed plane, one therefore has four clues for each of four other planes.

You are required to complete the cube to produce six magic squares each with a constant of 34. The second square down and the bottom square are both pan-diagonal.

Puzzle No. 92

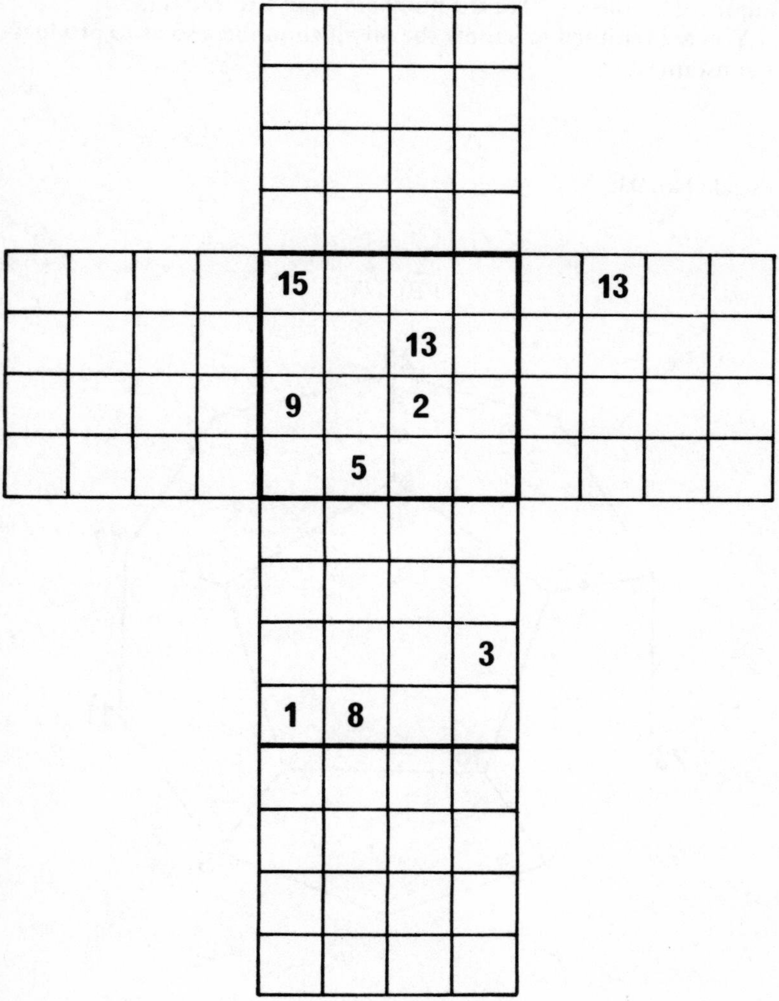

The diagrams below depict the front and rear views of a dodecahedron. The corners of the twelve pentagonal planes are numbered, utilising 20 of the numbers from 1 to 25.

You are required to supply the missing numbers so as to produce a constant of 65.

Puzzle No. 93

FRONT

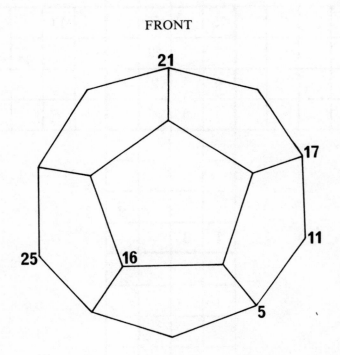

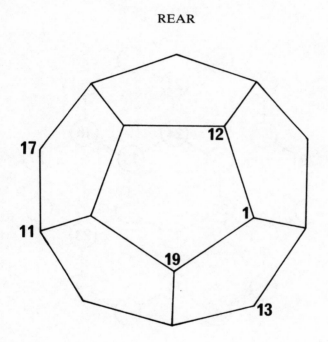

The diagrams below depict the front and rear views of an 'exploded' icosahedron comprising fourteen hexagons and six quadrangles. The corners of all fourteen hexagons are numbered consecutively from 1 to 36. You are required to supply the missing numbers to produce a constant of 111. Ignore the quadrangles.

Puzzle No. 94

FRONT

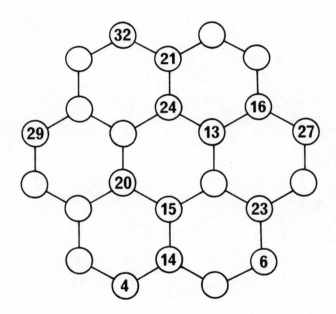

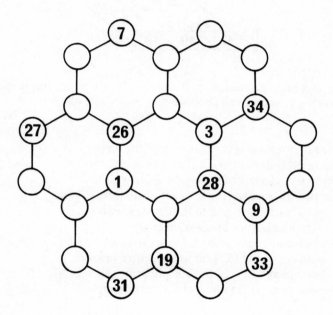

The diagram below shows a completed 3 power magic cube.

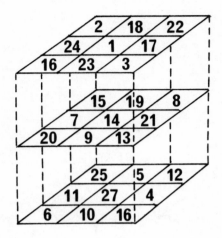

In this cube the numbers from 1 to 27 are so arranged that the following groupings all produce the constant of 42:

| | No. of groupings |
|---|---|
| the horizontal and vertical lines of the three grids | 18 |
| the vertical lines through the three grids | 9 |
| the two diagonals of the centre grid | 2 |
| the two diagonals from the centre squares, left and right, of the top grid to the centre squares, right and left, of the bottom grid | 2 |
| the two diagonals from the centre squares, top and bottom, of the top grid to the centre squares, bottom and top, of the bottom grid | 2 |
| the diagonals from each corner of the cube | 4 |
| | 37 |

The following two puzzles require the completion of similar 3 power magic cubes to produce a constant of 42 in each case. The five clues provided are sufficient to solve the puzzles without the need for trial and error.

Puzzle No. 95

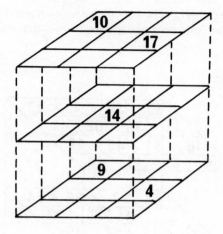

Puzzle No. 96

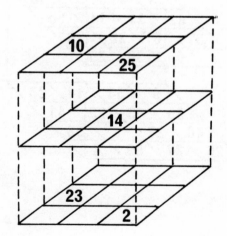

As one increases the size of the cube, so the number of groupings which produce the constant increases. The following diagram shows a 4 power magic cube in which the numbers 1 to 64 are so arranged that the following groupings all produce the constant of 130:

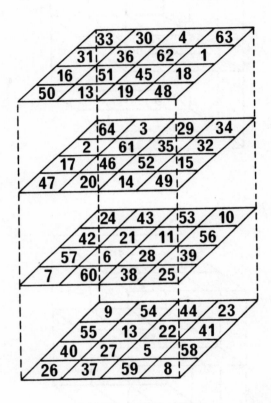

|  |  |
|---|---|
| the horizontal and vertical lines of each of the four grids | 32 |
| the vertical lines through all four grids | 16 |
| the diagonals from each corner of the cube | 4 |
| the four quarters of each grid as depicted | 16 |
| the four quarters of each grid depicted when the cube is in its other two possible positions | 32 |
|  | 100 |

In order to make the less obvious groupings clearer, the following diagram shows four groupings, marked A, B, C and D, each of which produces the constant. Note that only the diagonals of the cube produce the constant. The diagonals of the individual grids do not.

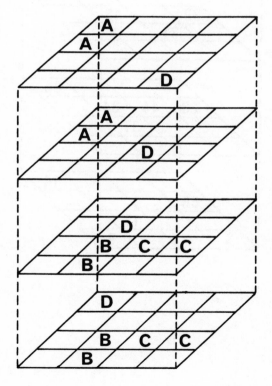

The following five puzzles involve similar 4 power magic cubes requiring completion to produce a constant of 130 in each case. The clues provided are sufficient to solve the puzzles without the need for trial and error.

Puzzle No. 97

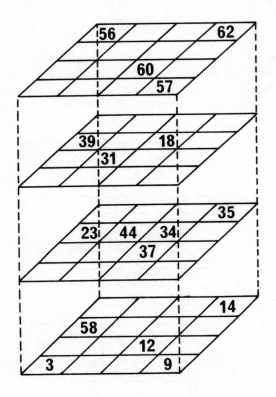

## Puzzle No. 98

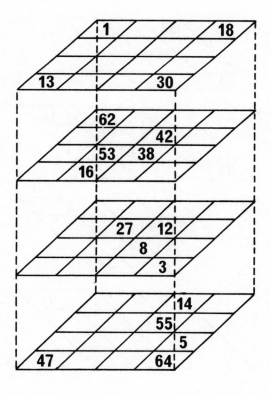

Puzzle No. 99

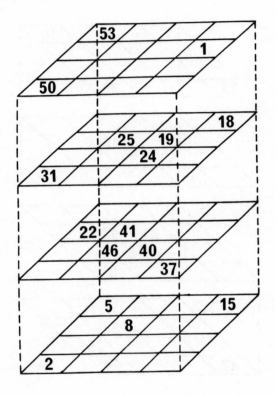

Puzzle No. 100

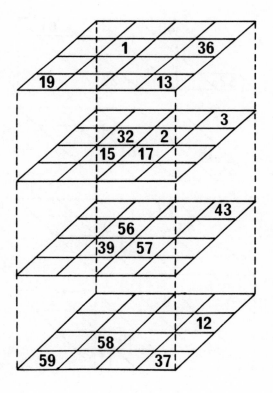

Puzzle No. 101

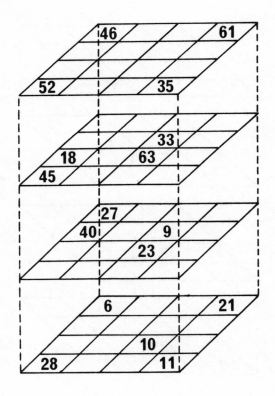

# Solutions

| 6 | 3 | 9 | 16 |
|---|---|---|---|
| 12 | 13 | 7 | 2 |
| 15 | 10 | 4 | 5 |
| 1 | 8 | 14 | 11 |

1

| 1 | 4 | 14 | 15 |
|---|---|---|---|
| 13 | 16 | 2 | 3 |
| 8 | 5 | 11 | 10 |
| 12 | 9 | 7 | 6 |

2

| 5 | 3 | 14 | 12 |
|---|---|---|---|
| 16 | 10 | 7 | 1 |
| 11 | 13 | 4 | 6 |
| 2 | 8 | 9 | 15 |

3

| 11 | 2 | 5 | 16 |
|---|---|---|---|
| 7 | 14 | 9 | 4 |
| 10 | 3 | 8 | 13 |
| 6 | 15 | 12 | 1 |

4

| 13 | 1 | 4 | 16 |
|---|---|---|---|
| 8 | 12 | 9 | 5 |
| 11 | 7 | 6 | 10 |
| 2 | 14 | 15 | 3 |

5

| 6 | 15 | 4 | 9 |
|---|---|---|---|
| 12 | 1 | 14 | 7 |
| 13 | 8 | 11 | 2 |
| 3 | 10 | 5 | 16 |

6

| 9 | 16 | 13 | 4 |
|---|---|---|---|
| 14 | 3 | 10 | 15 |
| 8 | 17 | 12 | 5 |
| 11 | 6 | 7 | 18 |

7

| 5 | 18 | 11 | 16 |
|---|---|---|---|
| 19 | 8 | 13 | 10 |
| 14 | 9 | 20 | 7 |
| 12 | 15 | 6 | 17 |

8

| 22 | 8 | 13 | 15 |
|---|---|---|---|
| 9 | 19 | 18 | 12 |
| 16 | 14 | 7 | 21 |
| 11 | 17 | 20 | 10 |

9

| 14 | 20 | 17 | 19 |
|---|---|---|---|
| 25 | 11 | 22 | 12 |
| 18 | 16 | 21 | 15 |
| 13 | 23 | 10 | 24 |

10

| 2 | 8 | 11 | 13 |
|---|---|----|----|
| 9 | 15 | 4 | 6 |
| 7 | 1 | 14 | 12 |
| 16 | 10 | 5 | 3 |

11

| 3 | 10 | 16 | 5 |
|---|----|----|---|
| 13 | 8 | 2 | 11 |
| 6 | 15 | 9 | 4 |
| 12 | 1 | 7 | 14 |

12

| 7 | 11 | 6 | 10 |
|---|----|---|----|
| 14 | 2 | 15 | 3 |
| 12 | 8 | 9 | 5 |
| 1 | 13 | 4 | 16 |

13

| 5 | 11 | 10 | 8 |
|---|----|----|---|
| 14 | 4 | 1 | 15 |
| 3 | 13 | 16 | 2 |
| 12 | 6 | 7 | 9 |

14

| 13 | 10 | 4 | 7 |
|----|----|---|----|
| 8 | 3 | 9 | 14 |
| 11 | 16 | 6 | 1 |
| 2 | 5 | 15 | 12 |

15

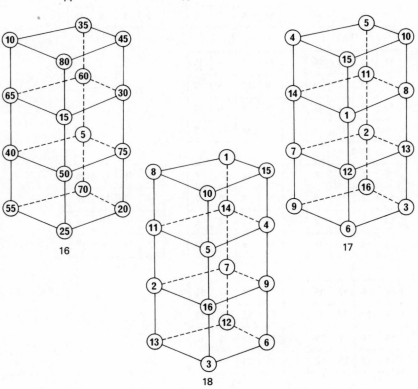

16

17

18

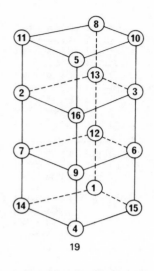

19

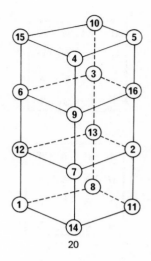

20

| S | P | I | N |
|---|---|---|---|
| H | A | T | E |
| E | V | E | R |
| D | E | M | O |

21

**RADISH**

| 16 | 10 | 5 | 3 |
|---|---|---|---|
| 7 | 1 | 14 | 12 |
| 9 | 15 | 4 | 6 |
| 2 | 8 | 11 | 13 |

| S | W | A | N |
|---|---|---|---|
| H | A | L | O |
| I | N | T | O |
| P | E | O | N |

22

**WHILST**

| 4 | 14 | 7 | 9 |
|---|---|---|---|
| 5 | 11 | 2 | 16 |
| 10 | 8 | 13 | 3 |
| 15 | 1 | 12 | 6 |

| T | H | I | S |
|---|---|---|---|
| R | A | C | E |
| A | V | O | N |
| P | E | N | T |

23

**CHIRPS**

| 2 | 9 | 16 | 7 |
|---|---|---|---|
| 8 | 15 | 10 | 1 |
| 13 | 6 | 3 | 12 |
| 11 | 4 | 5 | 14 |

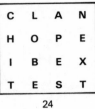

| | | | |
|---|---|---|---|
| C | L | A | N |
| H | O | P | E |
| I | B | E | X |
| T | E | S | T |

**BISHOP**

| 7 | 11 | 6 | 10 |
|---|---|---|---|
| 14 | 2 | 15 | 3 |
| 12 | 8 | 9 | 5 |
| 1 | 13 | 4 | 16 |

24

| | | | |
|---|---|---|---|
| S | P | A | T |
| H | A | L | E |
| I | R | O | N |
| N | E | E | D |

**POLISH**

| 15 | 6 | 9 | 4 |
|---|---|---|---|
| 12 | 1 | 14 | 7 |
| 2 | 11 | 8 | 13 |
| 5 | 16 | 3 | 10 |

25

| 4 | 20 | 16 | 14 | 11 |
|---|---|---|---|---|
| 18 | 5 | 24 | 1 | 17 |
| 19 | 3 | 13 | 23 | 7 |
| 9 | 25 | 2 | 21 | 8 |
| 15 | 12 | 10 | 6 | 22 |

26

| 9 | 8 | 26 | 12 | 15 |
|---|---|---|---|---|
| 5 | 17 | 24 | 21 | 3 |
| 18 | 22 | 14 | 6 | 10 |
| 25 | 7 | 4 | 11 | 23 |
| 13 | 16 | 2 | 20 | 19 |

27

| 13 | 11 | 9 | 25 | 22 |
|---|---|---|---|---|
| 14 | 24 | 5 | 20 | 17 |
| 28 | 26 | 16 | 6 | 4 |
| 15 | 12 | 27 | 8 | 18 |
| 10 | 7 | 23 | 21 | 19 |

28

| 21 | 10 | 19 | 24 | 16 |
|---|---|---|---|---|
| 6 | 28 | 11 | 23 | 22 |
| 29 | 27 | 18 | 9 | 7 |
| 14 | 13 | 25 | 8 | 30 |
| 20 | 12 | 17 | 26 | 15 |

29

| 28 | 26 | 15 | 13 | 18 |
|---|---|---|---|---|
| 8 | 16 | 17 | 30 | 29 |
| 31 | 21 | 20 | 19 | 9 |
| 11 | 10 | 23 | 24 | 32 |
| 22 | 27 | 25 | 14 | 12 |

30

| 3 | 11 | 22 | 9 | 20 |
|---|----|----|---|----|
| 24 | 10 | 18 | 1 | 12 |
| 16 | 2 | 14 | 25 | 8 |
| 15 | 23 | 6 | 17 | 4 |
| 7 | 19 | 5 | 13 | 21 |

31

| 9 | 25 | 13 | 1 | 17 |
|---|----|----|---|----|
| 11 | 2 | 19 | 10 | 23 |
| 20 | 8 | 21 | 12 | 4 |
| 22 | 14 | 5 | 18 | 6 |
| 3 | 16 | 7 | 24 | 15 |

32

| 14 | 23 | 22 | 11 | 5 |
|----|----|----|----|---|
| 12 | 6 | 15 | 24 | 18 |
| 25 | 19 | 8 | 7 | 16 |
| 3 | 17 | 26 | 20 | 9 |
| 21 | 10 | 4 | 13 | 27 |

33

| 23 | 16 | 14 | 7 | 25 |
|----|----|----|---|----|
| 9 | 27 | 20 | 18 | 11 |
| 15 | 13 | 6 | 29 | 22 |
| 26 | 24 | 17 | 10 | 8 |
| 12 | 5 | 28 | 21 | 19 |

34

| 29 | 26 | 18 | 15 | 7 |
|----|----|----|----|---|
| 20 | 12 | 9 | 31 | 23 |
| 11 | 28 | 25 | 17 | 14 |
| 22 | 19 | 16 | 8 | 30 |
| 13 | 10 | 27 | 24 | 21 |

35

| 8 | 16 | 4 | 12 | 25 |
|---|----|---|----|----|
| 2 | 15 | 23 | 6 | 19 |
| 21 | 9 | 17 | 5 | 13 |
| 20 | 3 | 11 | 24 | 7 |
| 14 | 22 | 10 | 18 | 1 |

36

| 12 | 16 | 25 | 4 | 8 |
|----|----|----|---|---|
| 5 | 9 | 13 | 17 | 21 |
| 18 | 22 | 1 | 10 | 14 |
| 6 | 15 | 19 | 23 | 2 |
| 24 | 3 | 7 | 11 | 20 |

37

| 14 | 16 | 5 | 22 | 8 |
|----|----|---|----|---|
| 2 | 23 | 9 | 11 | 20 |
| 6 | 15 | 17 | 3 | 24 |
| 18 | 4 | 21 | 10 | 12 |
| 25 | 7 | 13 | 19 | 1 |

38

| 20 | 11 | 7 | 23 | 4 |
|----|----|---|----|---|
| 8 | 24 | 5 | 16 | 12 |
| 1 | 17 | 13 | 9 | 25 |
| 14 | 10 | 21 | 2 | 18 |
| 22 | 3 | 19 | 15 | 6 |

39

| 24 | 20 | 11 | 7 | 3 |
|----|----|----|---|---|
| 12 | 8 | 4 | 25 | 16 |
| 5 | 21 | 17 | 13 | 9 |
| 18 | 14 | 10 | 1 | 22 |
| 6 | 2 | 23 | 19 | 15 |

40

| 25 | 4 | 19 | 18 | 33 | 12 |
|----|----|----|----|----|----|
| 36 | 6 | 2 | 34 | 5 | 28 |
| 16 | 29 | 14 | 23 | 8 | 21 |
| 20 | 10 | 26 | 11 | 27 | 17 |
| 1 | 32 | 35 | 3 | 31 | 9 |
| 13 | 30 | 15 | 22 | 7 | 24 |

41

| 21 | 2 | 18 | 15 | 35 | 20 |
|----|----|----|----|----|----|
| 29 | 31 | 1 | 33 | 7 | 10 |
| 23 | 34 | 12 | 13 | 3 | 26 |
| 14 | 5 | 25 | 24 | 32 | 11 |
| 8 | 30 | 36 | 4 | 6 | 27 |
| 16 | 9 | 19 | 22 | 28 | 17 |

42

| 24 | 1 | 17 | 19 | 36 | 14 |
|----|----|----|----|----|----|
| 5 | 28 | 34 | 10 | 4 | 30 |
| 22 | 6 | 11 | 25 | 31 | 16 |
| 13 | 35 | 20 | 18 | 2 | 23 |
| 32 | 33 | 3 | 27 | 9 | 7 |
| 15 | 8 | 26 | 12 | 29 | 21 |

43

| 11 | 2 | 26 | 20 | 35 | 17 |
|----|----|----|----|----|----|
| 29 | 34 | 1 | 5 | 33 | 9 |
| 23 | 30 | 14 | 16 | 7 | 21 |
| 18 | 10 | 19 | 25 | 27 | 12 |
| 8 | 4 | 36 | 32 | 3 | 28 |
| 22 | 31 | 15 | 13 | 6 | 24 |

44

| 16 | 2 | 20 | 25 | 35 | 13 |
|----|----|----|----|----|----|
| 36 | 9 | 29 | 27 | 6 | 4 |
| 21 | 30 | 17 | 12 | 7 | 24 |
| 14 | 5 | 26 | 19 | 32 | 15 |
| 1 | 31 | 8 | 10 | 28 | 33 |
| 23 | 34 | 11 | 18 | 3 | 22 |

45

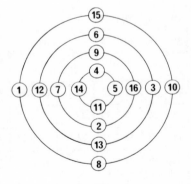

46

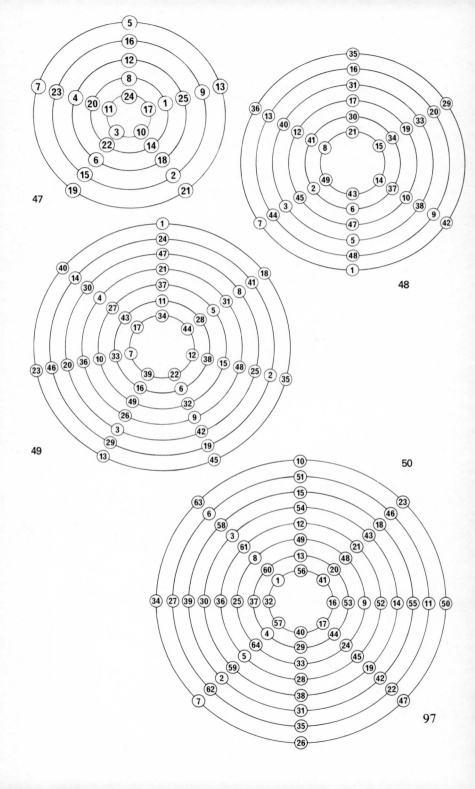

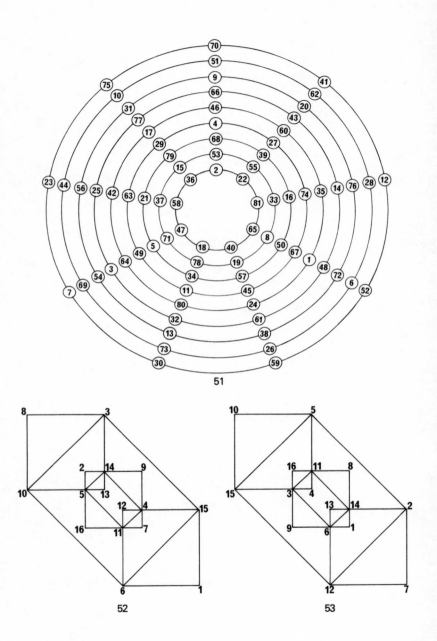

51

52

53

98

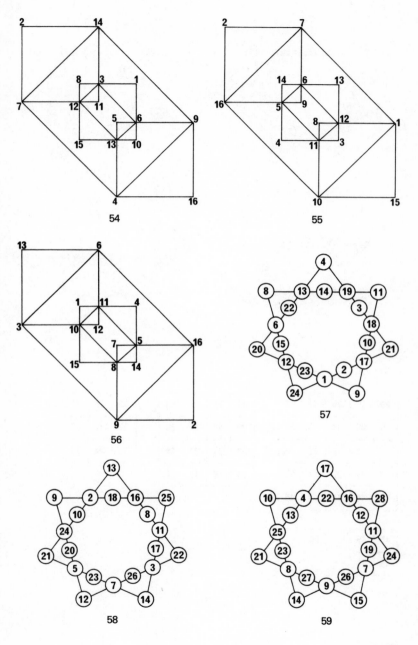

54

55

56

57

58

59

99

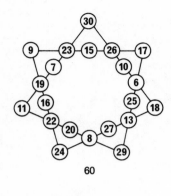

60

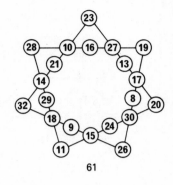

61

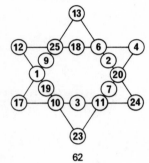

62

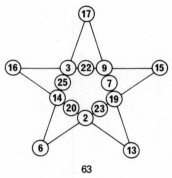

63

| 20 | 15 | 26 | 17 | 12 |
|----|----|----|----|----|
| 9 | 25 | 14 | 13 | 29 |
| 30 | 8 | 18 | 28 | 6 |
| 7 | 23 | 22 | 11 | 27 |
| 24 | 19 | 10 | 21 | 16 |

| 15 | 28 | 26 | 21 |
|----|----|----|----|
| 29 | 18 | 20 | 23 |
| 22 | 25 | 27 | 16 |
| 24 | 19 | 17 | 30 |

| 33 | 26 | 31 |
|----|----|----|
| 28 | 30 | 32 |
| 29 | 34 | 27 |

| 45 | 45 |
|----|----|
| 45 | 45 |

| 90 |
|----|

64

| 4 | 52 | 5 | 56 | 11 | 12 | 62 | 58 |
|---|---|---|---|---|---|---|---|
| 63 | 50 | 18 | 17 | 42 | 19 | 49 | 2 |
| 1 | 45 | 25 | 39 | 34 | 32 | 20 | 64 |
| 59 | 41 | 36 | 30 | 27 | 37 | 24 | 6 |
| 57 | 21 | 31 | 33 | 40 | 26 | 44 | 8 |
| 14 | 22 | 38 | 28 | 29 | 35 | 43 | 51 |
| 55 | 16 | 47 | 48 | 23 | 46 | 15 | 10 |
| 7 | 13 | 60 | 9 | 54 | 53 | 3 | 61 |

65

| 5 | 81 | 11 | 78 | 10 | 80 | 12 | 79 | 13 |
|---|---|---|---|---|---|---|---|---|
| 67 | 26 | 61 | 28 | 60 | 23 | 27 | 62 | 15 |
| 7 | 64 | 47 | 30 | 48 | 29 | 51 | 18 | 75 |
| 73 | 24 | 46 | 40 | 39 | 44 | 36 | 58 | 9 |
| 66 | 63 | 32 | 45 | 41 | 37 | 50 | 19 | 16 |
| 6 | 25 | 49 | 38 | 43 | 42 | 33 | 57 | 76 |
| 68 | 65 | 31 | 52 | 34 | 53 | 35 | 17 | 14 |
| 8 | 20 | 21 | 54 | 22 | 59 | 55 | 56 | 74 |
| 69 | 1 | 71 | 4 | 72 | 2 | 70 | 3 | 77 |

66

| 2 | 25 | 15 |
|---|---|---|
| 27 | 14 | 1 |
| 13 | 3 | 26 |

| 4 | 39 | 29 | 19 |
|---|---|---|---|
| 31 | 17 | 6 | 37 |
| 18 | 28 | 40 | 5 |
| 38 | 7 | 16 | 30 |

| 49 | 45 | 32 | 21 | 10 |
|---|---|---|---|---|
| 33 | 22 | 11 | 50 | 41 |
| 12 | 46 | 42 | 34 | 23 |
| 43 | 35 | 24 | 8 | 47 |
| 20 | 9 | 48 | 44 | 36 |

67

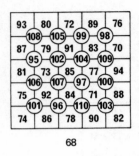

68

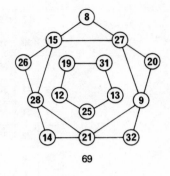

69

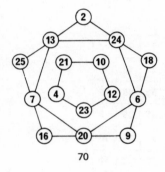

70

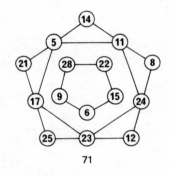

71

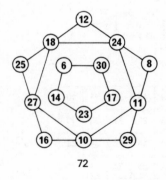

72

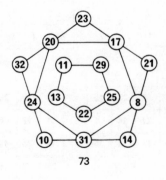

73

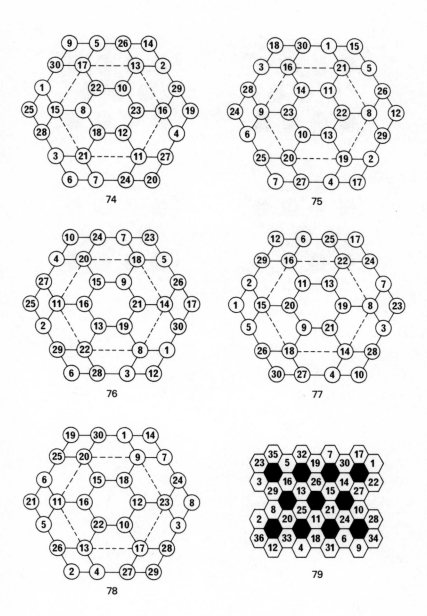

74

75

76

77

78

79

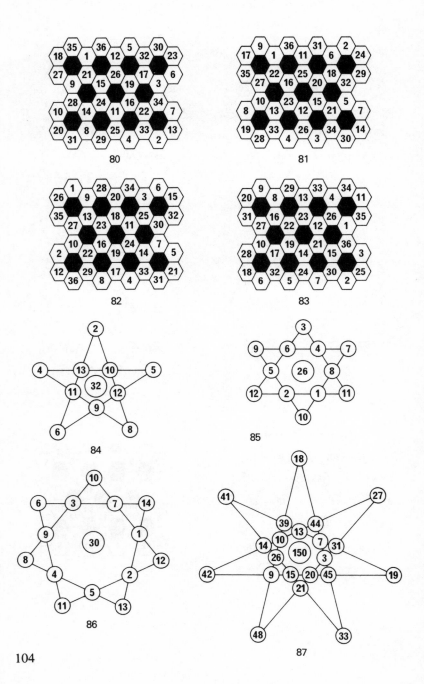

80

81

82

83

84

85

86

87

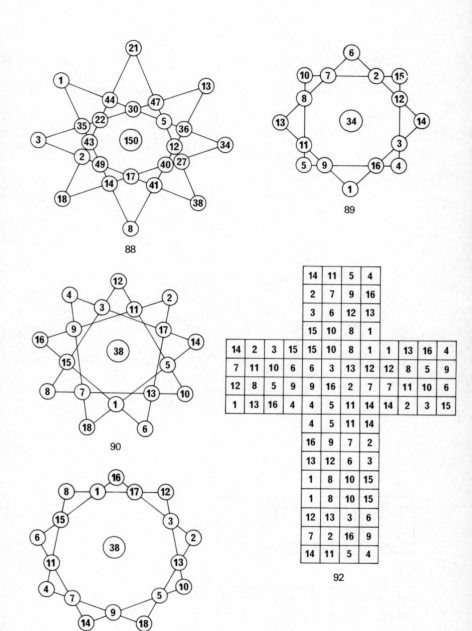

88

89

90

91

92

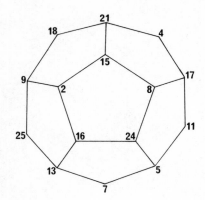
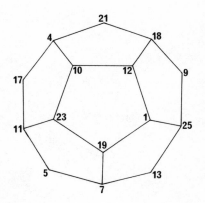

93

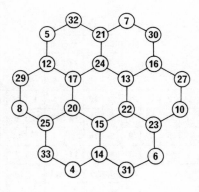
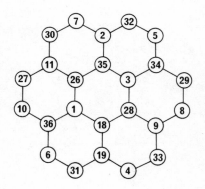

94

TOP

| 10 | 26 | 6 |
|----|----|----|
| 24 | 1  | 17 |
| 8  | 15 | 19 |

| 23 | 3  | 16 |
|----|----|----|
| 7  | 14 | 21 |
| 12 | 25 | 5  |

| 9  | 13 | 20 |
|----|----|----|
| 11 | 27 | 4  |
| 22 | 2  | 18 |

95

TOP

| 26 | 4  | 12 |
|----|----|----|
| 10 | 27 | 5  |
| 6  | 11 | 25 |

| 13 | 21 | 8  |
|----|----|----|
| 9  | 14 | 19 |
| 20 | 7  | 15 |

| 3  | 17 | 22 |
|----|----|----|
| 23 | 1  | 18 |
| 16 | 24 | 2  |

96